EASTBOURNE
AN ALPHABET

For Rob

A Journey In Print

Clare Dales

Clare Dales

Eastbourne An Alphabet - A Journey In Print

First paperback edition printed 2016 in the United Kingdom
A catalogue record for this book is available from the British Library

ISBN   978-1-5262-0172-0

Published by Clare Dales

For more copies of this book, please email: clare@claredales.com

Designed and Set by Clare Dales
Printed in Great Britain

Acknowledgements:
'O is For Oh No it Isn't': Based on an original costume design by Shelley Claridge for Eastbourne Theatres

for Thea

A is for Arrows And Axes

Eastbourne is at the Eastern end of The South Downs Way, a long distance path stretching along the ridge of the Downs towards Winchester. It was once a trading route for flint tools as far back as the Neolithic period, about 6,000 years ago. As the English Channel formed, the population settled down to farming, making tools from flints, clearing back woodland and grazing sheep on the land. The axes and flints made life easier and the sedentary population could perfect the design of implements for particular purposes; boring holes in hides, scraping and cutting. Some have been re-sharpened showing they kept and used their tools for years, much as we do today.

B is for Bathing Machine

Along the beach at Eastbourne, there were once hundreds of bathing machines, each with its own horse to manoeuvre it in and out of the sea. A Victorian lady might take to the waters for its health benefits. She would enter through one door of the machine, and emerge from the other end in full costume, to be plunged into the restorative sea by a dipper - a strong woman who would prevent the bather being swept out to sea.

C is for Camera Obscura

The Pier was opened on 13 June 1870 and is built
on stilts that rest in cups on the sea-bed allowing
the whole structure to move during rough weather.
Towards the seaward end of the 300metre long pier
is a Camera Obscura, part of the original range of
diversions on the pier.

This ingenious invention affords visitors a magical,
inverted 360˚ view of the town and out to sea. The
moving image is captured and transmitted via a
series of mirrors to a dish-shaped viewing surface
inside. The sight of moving images would have been a
wondrous delight as it still is today.

D is for Decorative Bricks

The Victorians ambitious programs of infrastructure, hotels and public buildings in the town allowed decoration in stone, glass and bricks. Decorative bricks are made by either throwing the clod of clay into a skillfully made mould, or by cutting and rubbing larger bricks into shape against a form work. Look around and you will find these fine examples.

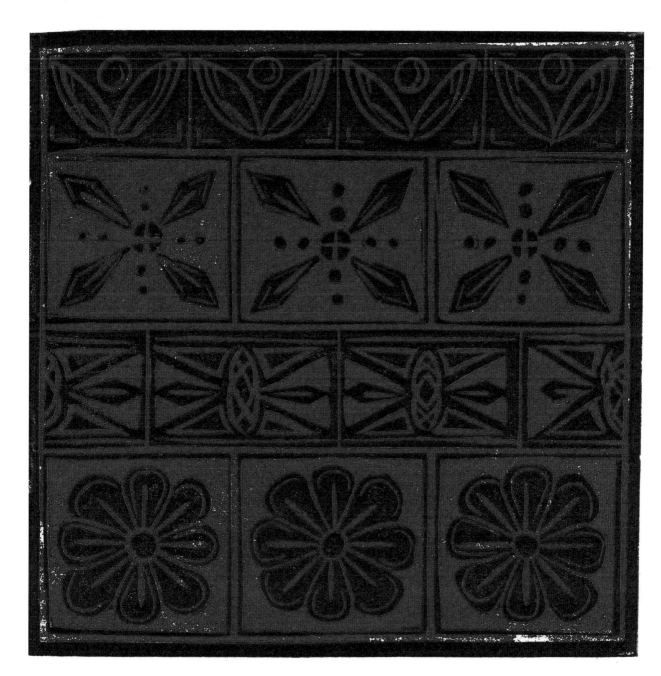

E is for English Channel

The English Channel is one of the busiest shipping channels in the world. All shipping must be registered to take to the seas. Vessels moored in Eastbourne are often registered at Newhaven, so bear the NN mark. Pleasure boats, Cruiseships, fishing boats, containerships, tankers and the Newhaven-Dieppe Ferry are plotted here - A live map of traffic at 12:00hrs 10th May 2015.

F is for Faience

Faience is the name given to glazed terracotta - a
kind of hard brick. Traditionally, moulds are carved
in wood, and the bricks carefully made and fired
to 1,100 degrees. They are then hand painted with
coloured glazes and fired again. The Bandstand is
faced with this durable material, lending a highly
decorative and colourful finish to the building.
The bandstand we enjoy today was built in 1935 to
replace 'The Birdcage', which had fallen into the sea.

G is for Gelateria

Gelato, made from milk and eggs is lighter than
ice-cream and a popular seaside treat. Antonio
Fusciardi emigrated from Italy and in 1965 he met
Anna Morelli; the couple married and set up the still
popular Gelateria in Marine Parade. The tiles outside
are distinctive piece of 1960's design, and local
landmark.

H is for Holywell

Holywell is known for it Italian Gardens. What is less
well known is that a submarine telegraph cable from
St Valery en Caux, Normandy, to Holywell was laid
in 1861, terminating in a landing shed on Beach No.1
They were part of the network of cables connecting
the Empire.

When the present gardens were laid out in 1922,
the cable was extended from the landing shed
and connected to terminal equipment in the small
building at the entrance to the gardens. The last
cables were laid in 1979 by the Cableship Alert.

SUBMARINE TELEGRAPH COMPANY

I Is for Ironwork

The distinctive bollards around Eastbourne, looking like smart soldiers standing on guard, were cast by the Morris Foundry. As you walk about the town, you will notice the foundry also cast drain covers, railings for verandahs, balconies and fencing, and distinctive square-based lamp posts. The foundry moved to Lewes in the 1830's and eventually became part of the Every Foundry, although Ebeneezer Morris retained a shop in Eastbourne.

J is for John Dory

Before William Cavendish, Duke of Devonshire
inherited land and built Victorian Eastbourne,
there was no more than a small fishing village
known as Seahouses, with Meads to the West and
a hinterland of agricultural land and grazing. The
sea has long been a source of food, and fishing boats
can be seen offshore, catching gurnard, john dory,
mackerel and a host of other fishes and crustaceans.

K is for Kidney Vetch

The Downland pasture has been continually grazed,
since being deforested around 6,000 years ago. The
characteristic skyline and rounded forms of the
Downs are maintained by the grazing of sheep. This
grazing keeps the grass low and rich in hundreds
of species of plant - One is the kidney vetch. This
is the sole food for the caterpillar of the Small Blue
butterfly. Measuring no more than 2cm across, the
small blue can be seen on the grass in Whitbread
Hollow to the Western end of the town.

L is for Ice Lolly

A refreshing ice-lolly. A fun treat and an essential element of a day out by the seaside!

M is for Milling

The Sussex countryside was once peppered with
mills. Essential to mill wheat for loaves, they also
crushed corn for livestock. The power of the wind
is captured by the sweeps, or sails, which turns a
gritty millstone against a fixed stone of identical
size.   Itinerate workers would go from mill to mill
to dress the stones, keeping them sharp. Several
examples of working mills still exist in Sussex.

N is for Napoleonic Fort

The Kent and Sussex coasts are home to Martello Towers, small defensive forts that were built across the British Empire during the 19th century. The threat of invasion from the South and East meant that each tower garrisoned around 20 men. The tower walls are thicker towards the sea to withstand attack, and feature rainwater collection to an underground tank - A well would be useless as it would be below sea level and saline. Chambers for storage and powder-making are below, with a living level below the flat roof housing the cannon.

O is for 'Oh No it Isn't'

The Devonshire Park district to the West of the town
centre was a planned playground. The Victorian
holiday makers and lucky residents could visit the
public baths, stroll in the pleasant park to the rear
of the theatres, or partake of roller blading to string
quartet accompaniments in the new Floral Hall. The
two theatres: The Devonshire Park Theatre in its
distinctive Italianate style, and the adjacent Winter
Gardens are still used, hosting annual pantomimes
and other diversions.

P is for Pippin

The Eastbourne Pippin is a crisp apple with a sweet
white flesh and a pinkish blush. It was grown by EA
Lindley in 1930 from the pip of a Newton Pippin.

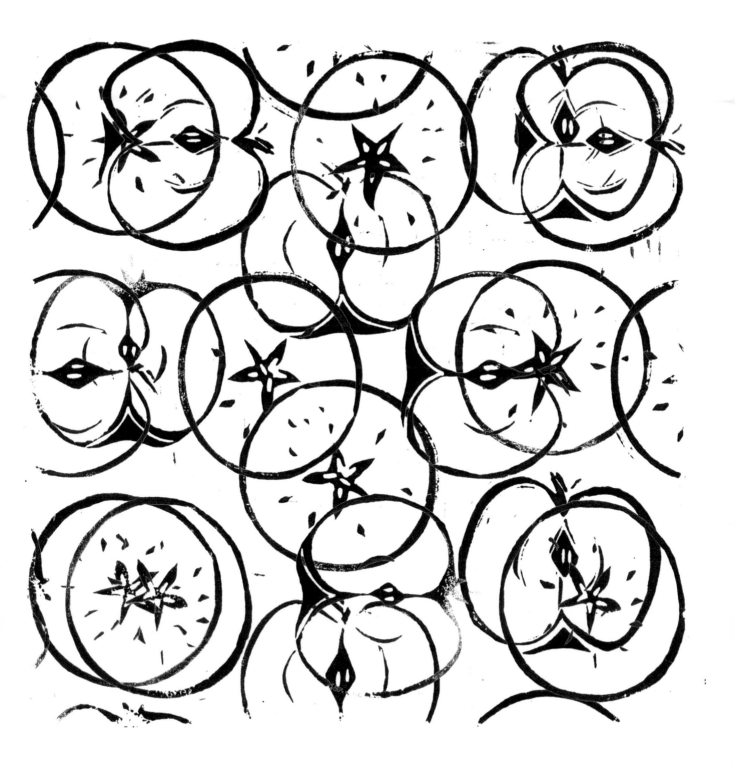

Q is for Queue Nails

Queues are the shoes worn by oxen, and the queue nails are made to secure them. Examples of both can be found anywhere in Eastbourne, as until the mid 19th Century much of what is now the Old Town and Meads was farmland. The road network follows the old field patterns with speculative building occupying a furlong; the land that could be ploughed by one man and an ox in one day.

R Is for Royal Sovereign Lighthouse

The English Channel is busy and hazardous.
Sandbanks and rocky reefs have been the end for
more than 200 vessels marked as wrecks on maritime
charts. The lighthouse is 6miles out to sea, and was
built in 1971, replacing a light vessel which had
marked the Royal Sovereign Shoal since 1875. At 36
metres tall, it was built in two sections on the beach
at Newhaven. The base and pillar were floated into
position and sunk on to a levelled area of the sea
bed. The cabin section contained accommodation
for the keepers who manned the lighthouse before
its automation in 1994. The flat upper deck of the
cabin section provides a helicopter landing platform.

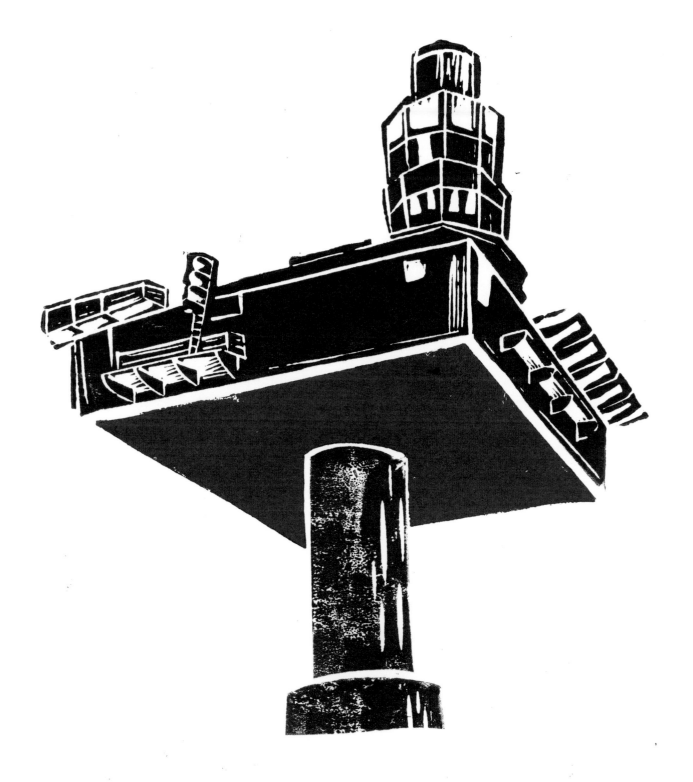

S is for Shipping Container

Standing on the shore looking towards France, there
will usually be a few container ships visible on the
horizon. Most of what we wear, use and much of
what we eat will have arrived via one of these ships.
The containers on one average ship if placed end-
to-end would make a line 40 miles long. Shipping
containers were first used at Chatham Docks as the
ChaCon (CHAtham CONtainer) in the 18th Century to
transport supplies.

T is for Tram & Taxi Hut

The drivers of the extensive tram network, and drivers of the numerous donkey carts and drays would have stopped for a warming cup of tea at this hut. The horses themselves were stabled in Old Town and each taxi would have around 7 changes of horse or donkey a day. The hut still serves sandwiches and snacks as it has for over 100 years.

U is for Umbrella

It may be necessary to shelter from the rain, or the sun, under an elegant parasol. Eastbourne is one of the sunniest places in England, but you might like to bring an umbrella anyway.

V is for Veteran Tree

A veteran tree is typically hundreds of years old, gnarled and home to a host of wildlife. They can stand alone in a field, creating a distinctive form, or be part of a woodland. Eastbourne has veteran oak and beech trees in the woods bordering the Downs and Hampden Park. Eastbourne is also home to the tallest Elm in Europe - It grows alongside Paradise Drive and stands 35 metres tall.

W is for Whelk

Common whelks and dog whelks proliferate along the shores. Lurking along low watermark tucked inside their impenetrable shell, they emerge to feed at high tide. Naturally drawn to dark enclosed spaces, whelks are harvested by being lured into a container with lobster or crab meat bait. Cooked and with a little vinegar they make a delicious snack.

X is for X-Ray

As you walk along the sea front, have you ever
wondered what lies behind the doors of the beach
huts? Beac huts are places to store, to shelter from
the wind and rain, to nap away from the strong
summer sun, and watch the activity of the beach
and sea. Given the opportunity to peek inside, the
individuality is often a surprise and delight, and
is a uniquely English feature of the promenade.

Y is for Model Yacht Club

In Princes Park, to the Eastern end of the sea front, there is a purpose-built lake for sailing model yachts and other vessels. Until the creation of Princes Park in 1921, the area was known as The Crumbles and then Gilbert's Recreation Ground. The Crumbles is an area of brackish water and shingle. The boating lake is fed by a river, but has a sluice to prevent it from draining at low tide.

Z is for Zooid

These are often seen washed up on the shore and
presumed to be seaweed. They are in fact skeletons
of colonial animals, known as zooids, which are
barely visible to the naked eye. Each tiny sessile
organism lives in a pouch. The animal pushes open
a microscopic lid when the tide submerges them,
and wafts its tentacles through the water for food.

Clare Dales

Clare Dales is a Sussex printmaker, publishing and exhibiting for over 14 years. With a background in archaeology and architecture, her range of subjects is diverse. Techniques often encompass a mix of lino print, collage, drawing and mono print. Clare also produces textiles and stationery.

clare@claredales.com

MR. TIGHTARSE
AT CHRISTMAS TIME

Roger Mee-Senseless

DISCLAIMER:

This is not a Mr Men book.
It is unsuitable for
young children.

If, however, you have the sense
of humour of a 7 year old and
are simply trapped in an
adult's body then it will
be entirely suitable.

Critical acclaim for Mister Tightarse -

"THE FUNNIEST THING I'VE SEEN SINCE
LAST TUESDAY, WHEN I SAW SOMEONE
WALK INTO A LAMP POST."
BARRY IRELAND, BARRY ISLAND

"I LAUGHED SO MUCH THAT A LITTLE BIT OF
DRIBBLE CAME OUT OF MY NOSE, I SHOULD
PROBABLY GO TO THE DOCTORS
ABOUT THAT ACTUALLY."
IVOR SOREBOTTOM, WETWANG

"WOULD MAKE A GREAT PRESENT FOR
SOMEONE YOU DON'T LIKE VERY MUCH."
POLLY VINYL-CHLORIDE, CRUDWELL

Ahh, Christmas.

The season of goodwill.

The time to give thoughtful gifts and spend time with loved ones.

To celebrate the birth of our Christ.

BOLLOCKS TO THAT!

It was the 2nd of November and Mr Tightarse was browsing around the sales.

Over the speakers came the first few beats of 'Last Christmas' by Wham. This made Mr Tightarse very angry indeed.

"Why do you have to ram this shit down everyone's throat? Aye? Every year I swear it gets earlier. I'm telling you, it's a fucking joke. It should be banned until Christmas Eve . Why don't you just say to hell with it and start playing them in August? In fact, just never stop playing them. It's just one big commercial shitstorm nowadays, nobody actually knows what Christmas means anymore."

"So, would you like to buy a mince pie then?" came the reply.

Mr Tightarse was at his 5 year old son's school fair.

"Did you cook them yourself?" asked Mr Tightarse.

"Yes, they were freshly cooked by the children in the school kitchen this morning," replied the boy.

"Yeh, I thought so," said Mr Tightarse. "They look like shit, I wouldn't eat one if you paid me."

This conversation was overheard by on of the teachers and Mr Tightarse was asked to leave the premises.

"Good, I didn't want to come anyway," was his response. "And by the way, your poster looks like it says 'minge pies'."

He ambled home and shouted at a little Robin along the way.

When he returned home he noticed on the mantelpiece that Mrs Tightarse, his long suffering wife, had brought the children an advent calendar each.

I'm not having that, thought Mr Tightarse. They'll get rotten teeth and then muggins here will have to take them to the dentist.

So he proceeded to empty all of the chocolates from the windows, swallowing each one whole. He replaced them with handwritten 'unmotivational quotes' like:

1. Every silver lining has a cloud
2. Why do today what you can do tomorrow?

And his personal favourite,

3. Whatever doesn't kill you makes you stronger (unless it's a degenerative muscle wasting disease)

Under the window for Christmas Day Mr Tightarse had written: 'Santa isn't real, fool.'

His next job on the list was to go and sort out a Christmas tree. Lots of families like to make this into an event where they can go and choose the perfect tree together.

Mr Tightarse had learnt that this was not the way to do it. It took bloody ages for everyone to agree and would inevitably cost him a shit tonne of money, for something that would be dead within weeks.

So he would sneak out by himself and head down to the local petrol station (tailgating to save petrol) where he would choose the most runty looking tree possible. These would normally be pretty cheap anyway but Mr Tightarse had got a plan to get it even cheaper.

The worst one of these was in August when Mr Tightarse decided to stop buying toilet roll. He had worked out that they could save hundreds of pounds over a year by using 'reusable paper' instead.

"Lots of people around the world use towels instead," he explained.

But Mr Tightarse had gone one step further. He had taken 3 squares of regular toilet paper and ran it through a laminator, thus making it 'permanently reusable'.

Christmas morning soon arrived. Mr Noisy, who lived next door to Mr Tightarse was woken by a strange noise.

'Who the fuck is making such a racket on Christmas morning? That's meant to be MY job!'

"WHAT ARE YOU DOING DOWN THERE!?" hollered Mr Noisy.

"What does it look like? I'm melting the snow so that the kids can't play with it," came the reply.

Mr Tightarse was using a hairdryer plugged into 3 extension leads to melt all of the snow in his garden. It took him over 2 hours but when he was finished he was safe in the knowledge that his garden, at least, would be a fun free zone.

When he had finished he headed back indoors and asked Mrs Tightarse to wrap a present for him.

"Make sure you do it neatly," he demanded.

Mrs Tightarse dutifully wrapped the present and added a little foil bow to the top, before handing it back to him.

The family then gathered around the Christmas tree in the living room so that they could open all of the presents.

The children sat on the floor and the adults on the sofa. The presents were then passed in turn to the relevant people.

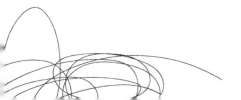

Terry, the eldest child, was the first to open his present. Excitedly he ripped the paper off which revealed a large box with a picture of a flat screen TV on it. He tore open the suspiciously light package and inside found... absolutely nothing.

Mr Tightarse noticed his puzzled expression and explained: "You kids are only ever interested in the box anyway so I returned the TV and just kept the box."

"But Dad, I'm 19. I don't play with boxes anymore!?"

"Do you know your problem?" replied Mr Tightarse. "You're always moaning."

The rest of the family looked at each other knowingly.

The next to open their present was Tasmin, Mr Tightarse's 9 year old daughter.

"Remind me what you wanted again?" he prompted.

"The new iphone! I really, really, really want one!" she replied in a flash. "All my friends have got one."

"Yeh, I thought it was," said Mr Tightarse, who then handed her a small rectangular shaped present, that looked and felt promisingly phone-like.

She made short work of the wrapping paper, she opened the lid to the box and then stopped in her tracks.

"Wow, erm, thanks Dad. What is it?"

"That, my darling daughter, is my old Nokia 5510. I tell you what, they don't make phones like that anymore. Literally. It's as solid as a rock that. It's got snake on it and everything. Plus, if anyone tries to steal it you can just hit em with it."

The phone was practically the same size as her and it took all of her might to hold it to her ear.

"There's no credit on it though, so you'll have to get that yourself," he added.

Next up was the 5 year old son, Toby.

Toby was passed a slim envelope that he needed help to open. "Here, let me," said Mr Tightarse. "We haven't got all fucking day."

He passed a card back to Toby. Inside the card was a wad of gift vouchers. They were about 10 of them each worth £20.

The family were shocked into silence, this was without doubt, the single most generous gift that Mr Tightarse had ever given ANYONE.

"Hold on a second," said Mrs Tightarse. "Aren't those Woolworths vouchers?"

"They are indeed," replied Mr Tightarse. "£200 pounds worth of them!" he beamed.

"The same Woolworths that hasn't existed since 2015?"

"Erm, yeh. That one," came the reply.

"So he can't actually spend them then? she questioned.

"Jesus Christ, what's with all of the questions? Honestly, you try to do something nice..."

Mrs Tightarse was next up to open her present. She was handed a familiar looking package. It was the very present that she had wrapped herself moments earlier.

With some curiosity she opened the box and the gift was revealed.

"Oh, it's a new hair dryer. Jesus Christ it's hot! And I think it's burnt out. It's smoking and gone black."

"It'll be fine. Right where are my presents then?" said Mr Tightarse impatiently.

His pile was by far the largest. The rest of the family had long since given up trying to second guess what he would actually like so he now brought all of his own presents. During the next 45 minutes they watched on as Mr Tightarse opened present after present. There was everything from bottles of single malt whisky, a new laptop, camera, games console, books, clothes and a new iphone.

"Well, I suppose that's all I've got then," hurrumphed Mr Tightarse, when he had finally opened the last present. "I'll probably end up taking all of this back tomorrow..."

The smell of cooking wafted in from the kitchen. In a vain attempt to instil some Christmas spirit into him Mrs Tightarse had asked her husband if he would like to cook Christmas dinner.

Uncharacteristically, he had agreed and strangely hadn't asked for any help.

He disappeared into the kitchen while the rest of the family huddled around Tasmin's 1.2 inch screen to play snake on her 'new' phone.

After much clattering, banging and swearing Mr Tightarse emerged from the kitchen with 5 steaming plates on a silver tray.

He served the first plate onto the table.

It was a plate of steaming hot, perfectly cooked, buttered Brussels sprouts

At least we are going to have a nice meal together, thought the rest of the family. The second plate was served which also contained Brussels sprouts. This was followed by a third and a forth.

There was also a cloche which, when the lid was lifted, revealed a grand, Ferroro Rocher esque pyramid of sprouts for 'pudding'.

"You see, sprouts were on the special buys at Aldi, they were only 20p a kilo so I bought 15 bags."

"That'll be breakfast, dinner and tea all over the holidays sorted," he said.

The rest of the family looked dumbfounded.

"Cheer up," said Mr Tightarse.

"It's Christmas!"

WIN WIN WIN!

If you enjoyed this book then please
consider leaving a review on Amazon.
Doing so will automatically enter you
into a competition to win a year's
supply of chicken beaks.

Good luck.

Printed in Great Britain
by Amazon

14704733R00027